Back to Basics

MATHS

for 6-7 year olds

BOOK TWO

George Rodda

1 2 3 4 5 6 7 8 9 10

Finish writing the numbers.

11 12 13 14 15 16   20

21   23   25   27   29 30

31 32   34   36   38 39 40

41   44 45   48   50

Count these penguins.

penguins

2

Write the numbers for these penguins.

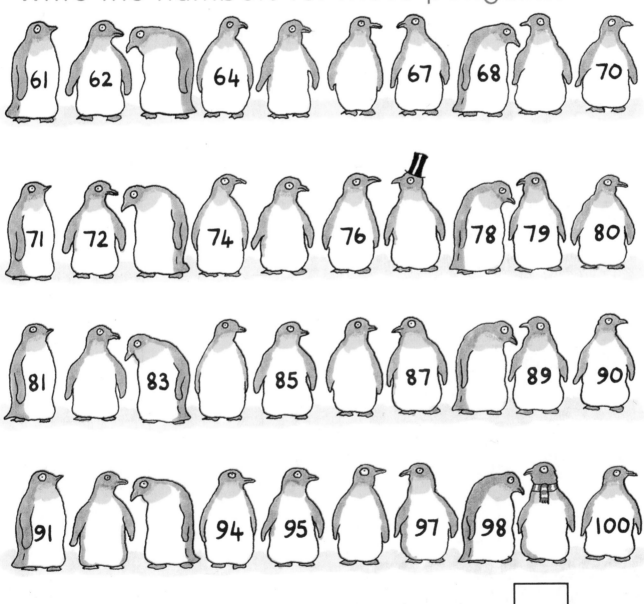

Which penguin is wearing a hat? ☐

Which one is wearing a scarf? ☐

3

Thirty has won.

twenty 20

Count the flowers.

thirty ☐

forty ☐

fifty ☐

sixty ☐

seventy ☐

eighty ☐

ninety ☐

4

one two three four five

six seven eight nine ten

11 eleven

22 twenty-two

33 thirty-three

44 forty-four

55 fifty-five

77 seventy-seven

66 sixty-six

88 eighty-eight

99 ninety-nine

Fill in the colours.

5

Dominoes

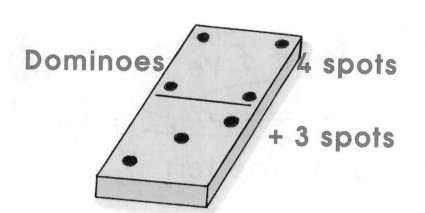 4 spots

+ 3 spots

 7 spots

Add the spots.

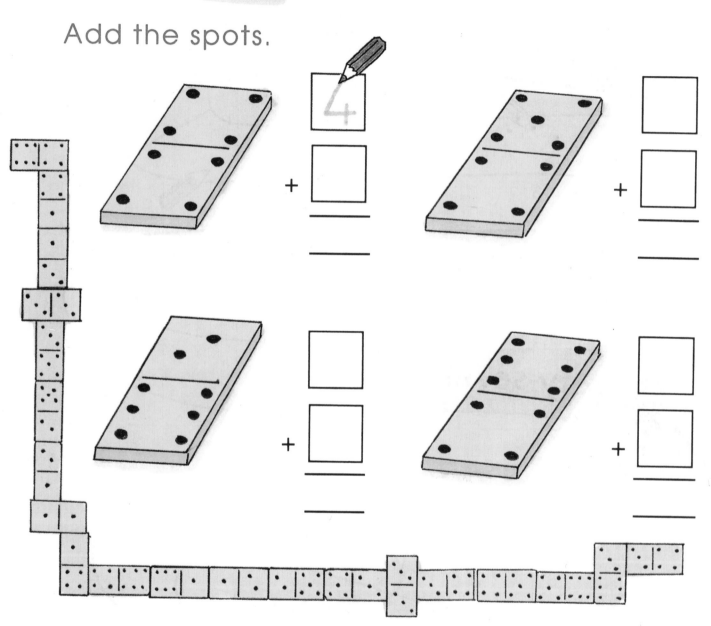

4
+5
___
___

5
+5
___
___

6
+5
___
___

6
+6
___
___

6

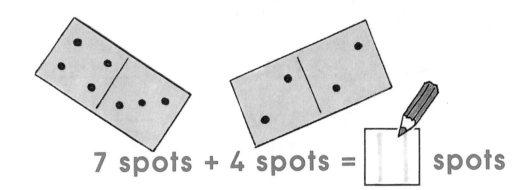

7 spots + 4 spots = **11** spots

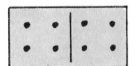

7 spots + ☐ spots = ☐ spots

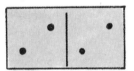

☐ spots + ☐ spots = ☐ spots

☐ spots + ☐ spots = ☐ spots

Add

5 + 6 = ☐   10 + 9 = ☐

9 + 6 = ☐   8 + 5 = ☐

5 + 7 = ☐   10 + 10 = ☐

12 fish

3 swam away

```
  12  fish
-  3  fish
――――――
   9  fish
```

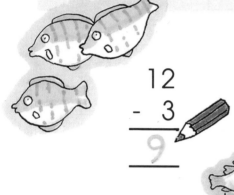

```
  12
-  3
――――
   9
```
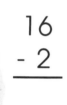

```
  12
-  2
――――
```

```
  12
- 10
――――
```

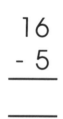

```
  16
-  2
――――
```

```
  16
-  3
――――
```

```
  16
-  4
――――
```

```
  16
-  5
――――
```

```
  16
-  6
――――
```

```
  16
-  7
――――
```

```
  19
-  9
――――
```

```
  19
- 10
――――
```

```
  19
-  8
――――
```

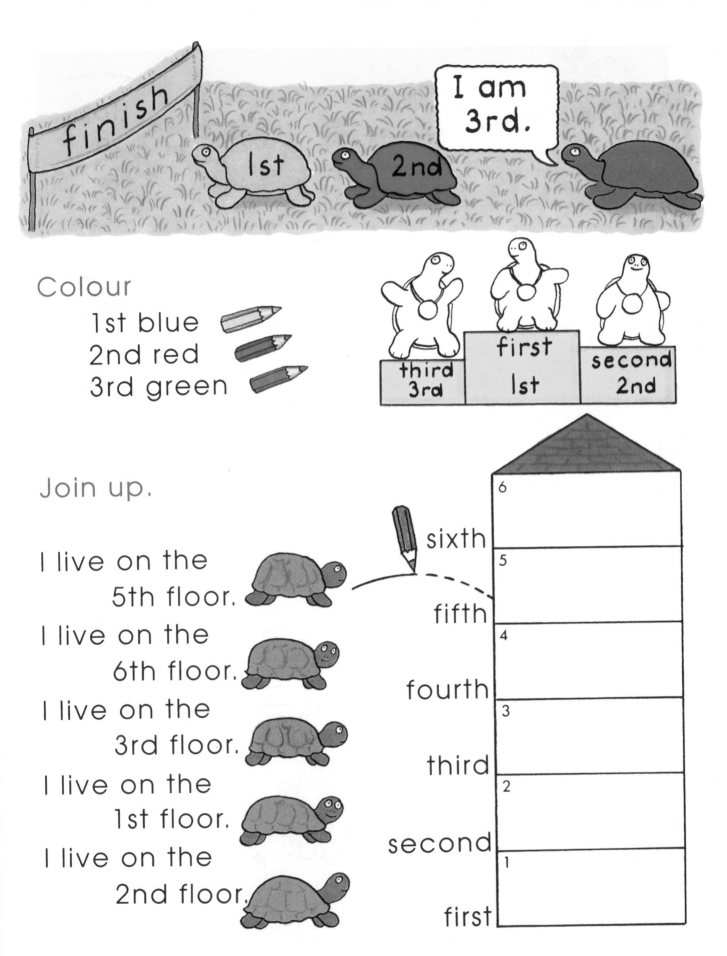

Colour

1st blue
2nd red
3rd green

Join up.

I live on the
   5th floor.

I live on the
   6th floor.

I live on the
   3rd floor.

I live on the
   1st floor.

I live on the
   2nd floor.

Draw yourself in the empty room.

9

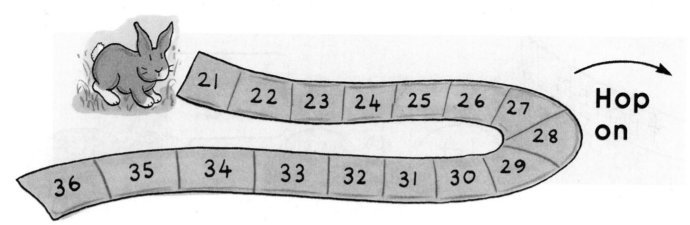

Hop on

start	hop on	finish
32	→ 2 →	34

start	hop on	finish		start	hop on	finish
21	→ 2 →	23		28	→ 2 →	
21	→ 3 →			30	→ 3 →	
21	→ 4 →			32	→ 3 →	
21	→ 5 →			30	→ 6 →	

Play this game.

start
21

4 **hop on**

finish
25

10

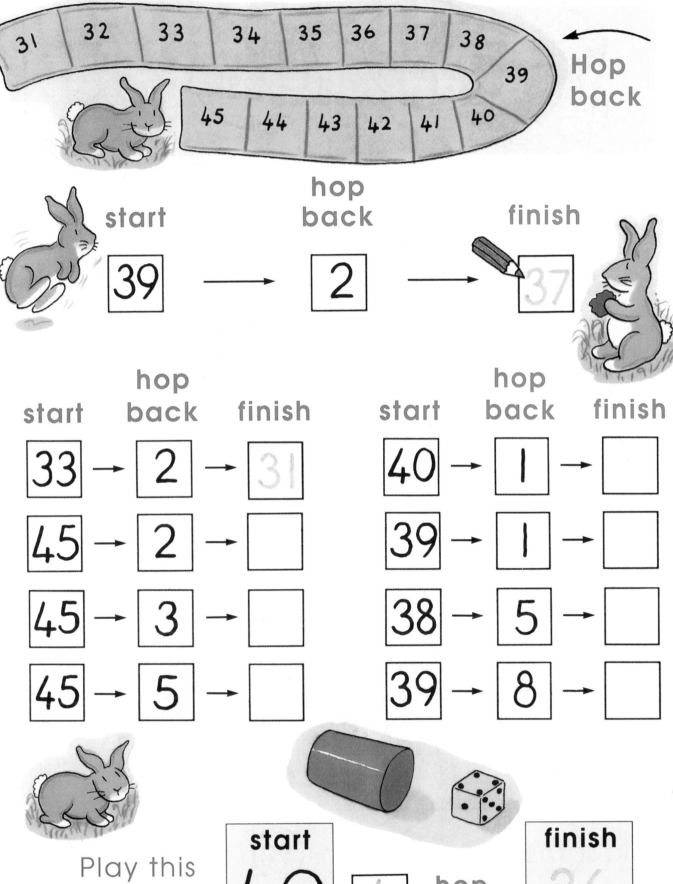

31	32	33	34	35	36	37	38

Hop back

45	44	43	42	41	40	39

start	hop back	finish
39 →	2 →	37

start	hop back	finish		start	hop back	finish
33 →	2 →	31		40 →	1 →	
45 →	2 →			39 →	1 →	
45 →	3 →			38 →	5 →	
45 →	5 →			39 →	8 →	

Play this game.

start		hop back	finish
40	4		36

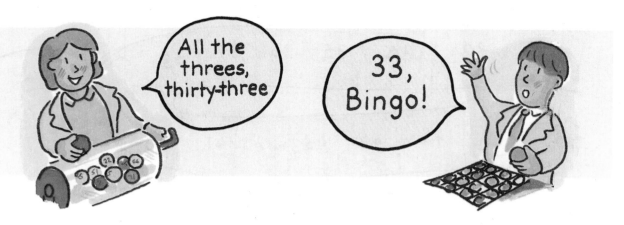

Fill in the numbers on the grid.

1	2	3	4	5		7		9	
11		13	14		16				20
21				25	26			29	
31			34	35		37			40
41									
	52	53						59	
61			64				68		
71		73		75		77		79	
	82		84		86		88		90
91								99	100

Colour these balls green ⟨90⟩ ⟨79⟩ ⟨68⟩ ⟨53⟩

and these balls red. ⟨35⟩ ⟨84⟩ ⟨73⟩ ⟨82⟩ ⟨44⟩

12

Bouncing ball

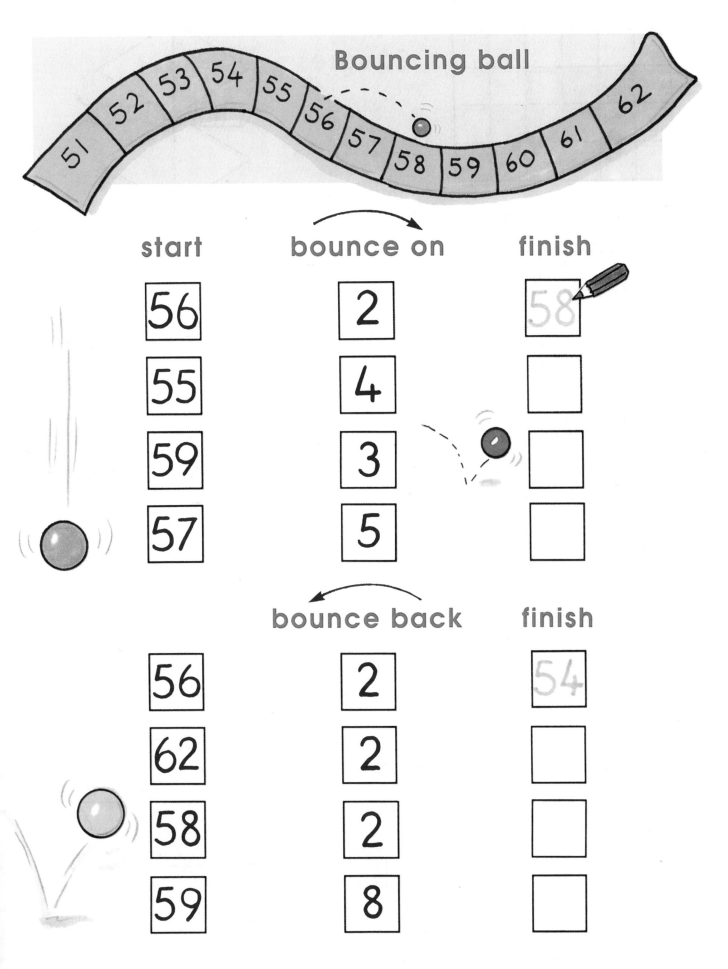

start	bounce on	finish
56	2	58
55	4	
59	3	
57	5	

	bounce back	finish
56	2	54
62	2	
58	2	
59	8	

13

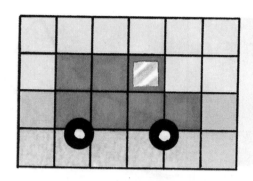

Squares and triangles

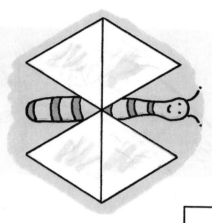

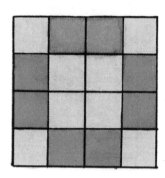

How many blue squares?

How many red squares?

How many squares altogether? 16

How many blue triangles?

How many red triangles?

How many triangles altogether?

Make your own pattern.

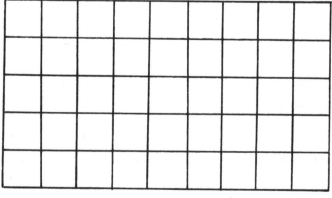

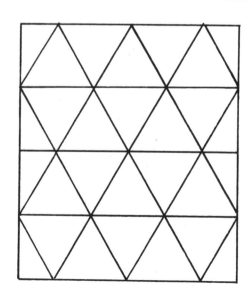

14

Mirror patterns

Colour your patterns.

Weather

sun rain cloud fog

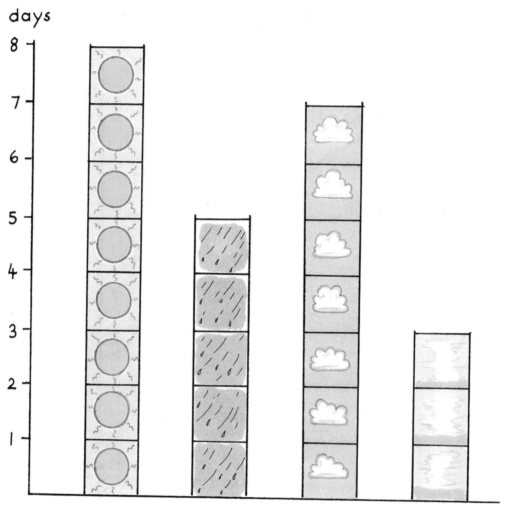

days

How many days . . .

rain? ☐   sun? ☐

fog? ☐   cloud? ☐

16

April showers

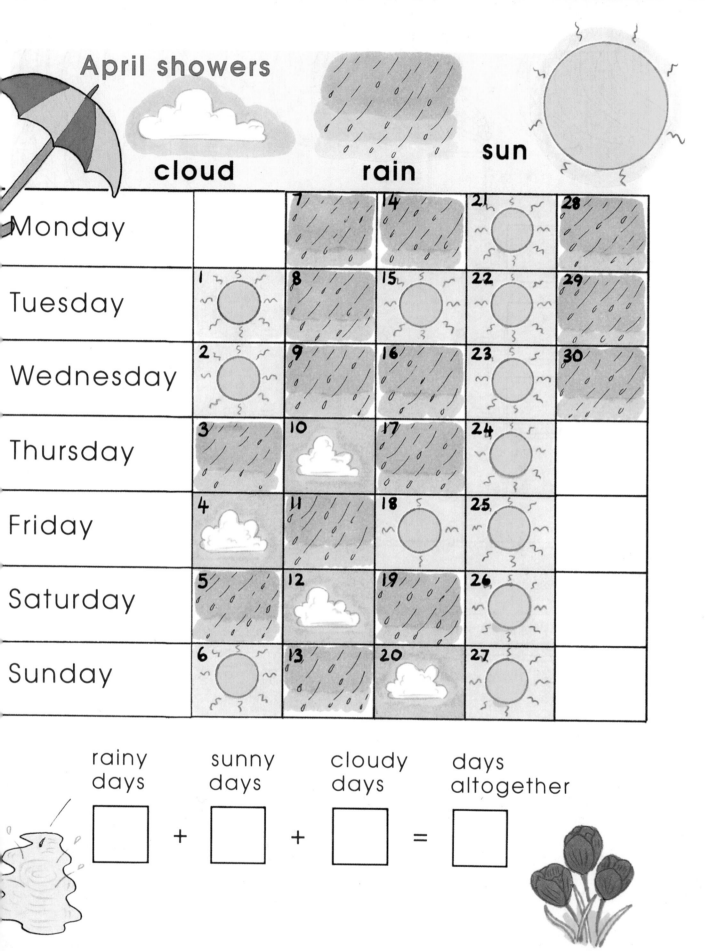

	cloud	rain	rain	sun	sun
Monday		7	14	21	28
Tuesday	1	8	15	22	29
Wednesday	2	9	16	23	30
Thursday	3	10	17	24	
Friday	4	11	18	25	
Saturday	5	12	19	26	
Sunday	6	13	20	27	

rainy days ☐ + sunny days ☐ + cloudy days ☐ = days altogether ☐

Make your own weather chart.

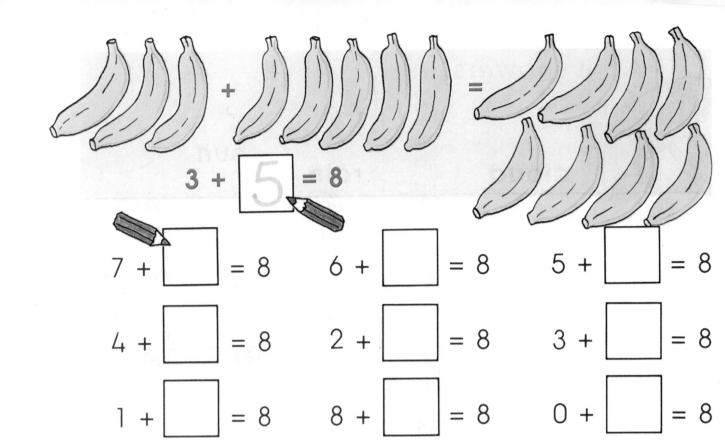

3 + 5 = 8

7 + ☐ = 8   6 + ☐ = 8   5 + ☐ = 8

4 + ☐ = 8   2 + ☐ = 8   3 + ☐ = 8

1 + ☐ = 8   8 + ☐ = 8   0 + ☐ = 8

Join up the dots to make 8.

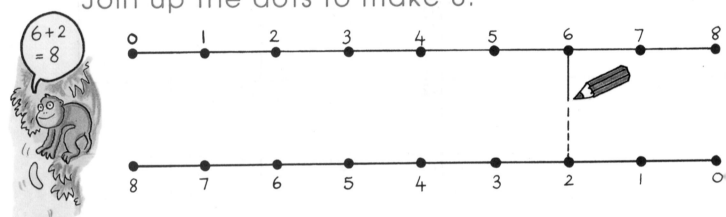

6 + 2 = 8

Join up the dots to make 8.

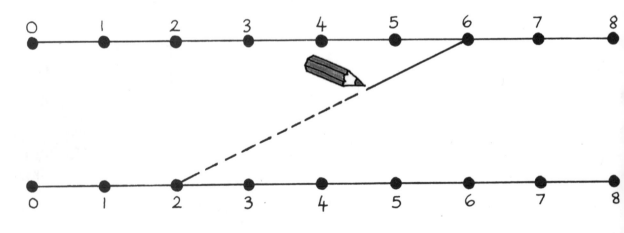

strawberry

pear

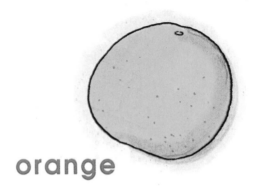
orange

Finish the patterns.

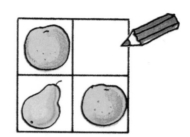

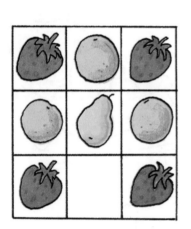

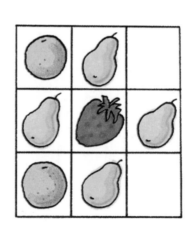

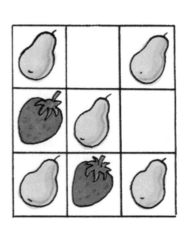

Make your own patterns.

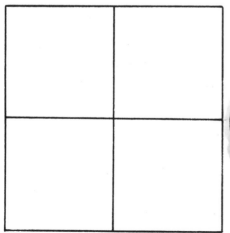

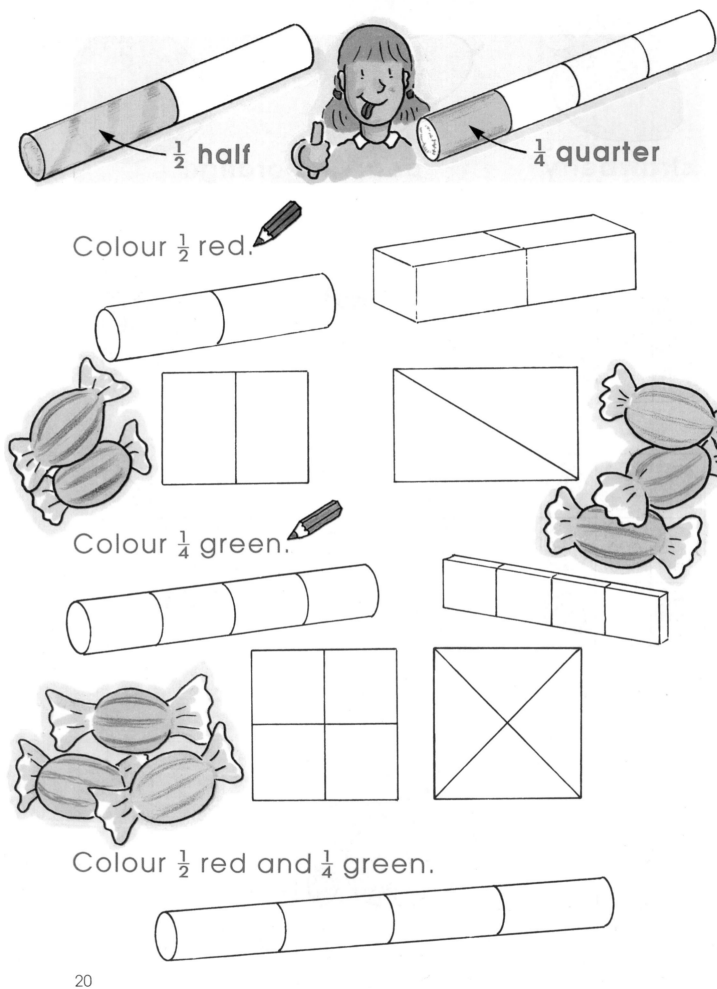

$\frac{1}{2}$ **half**

$\frac{1}{4}$ **quarter**

Colour $\frac{1}{2}$ red.

Colour $\frac{1}{4}$ green.

Colour $\frac{1}{2}$ red and $\frac{1}{4}$ green.

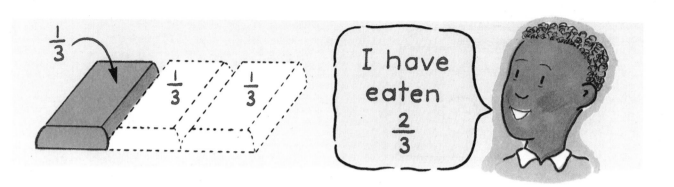

Colour $\frac{1}{3}$ brown.

Colour $\frac{1}{3}$ pink.

Colour $\frac{1}{3}$ yellow.

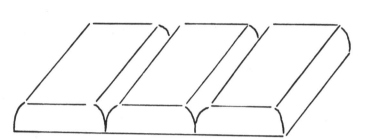

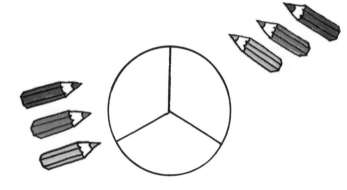

Draw round $\frac{1}{3}$ of the sweets.

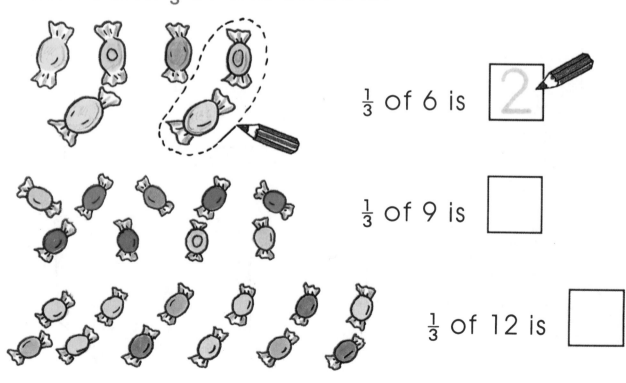

$\frac{1}{3}$ of 6 is [2]

$\frac{1}{3}$ of 9 is [ ]

$\frac{1}{3}$ of 12 is [ ]

5p + 5p = 10p

in the box

Put coins in
the boxes
to make 10p.

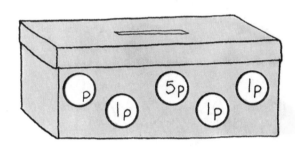

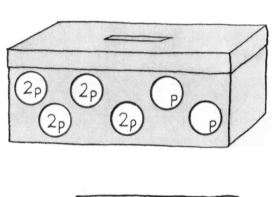

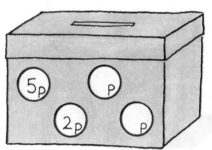

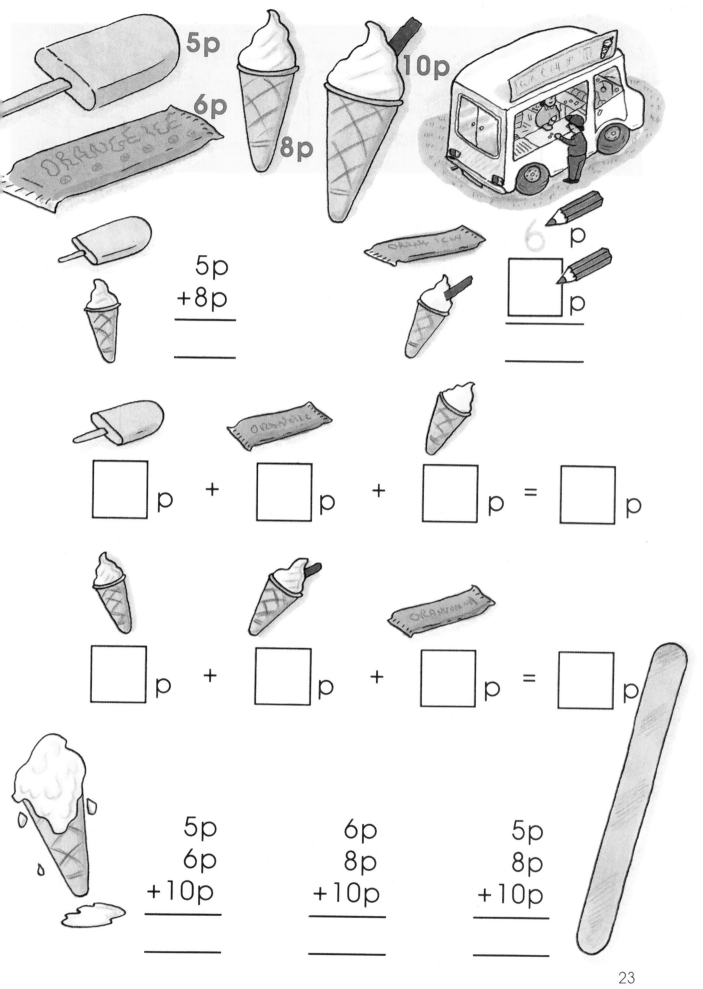

5p
6p
8p
10p

5p
+8p
_____
_____

6 p

☐ p
_____

☐ p + ☐ p + ☐ p = ☐ p

☐ p + ☐ p + ☐ p = ☐ p

5p   6p   5p
6p   8p   8p
+10p   +10p   +10p
____   ____   ____
____   ____   ____

23

Don't forget your change.

From 10p

change 2 p

From

 10p

 9p

change ☐ p

 10p

7p change ☐ p

10p 6p change ☐ p

10p - 1p = ☐ p   10p - 2p = ☐ p

10p - 3p = ☐ p   10p - 4p = ☐ p

10p - 5p = ☐ p   10p - 6p = ☐ p

10p - 7p = ☐ p   10p - 8p = ☐ p

10p - 9p = ☐ p   10p - 10p = ☐ p

You need more change.

From 20p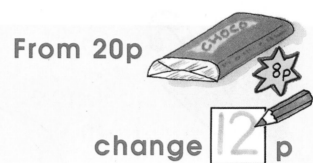

change 12 p

From

  change ☐ p

  7p change ☐ p

20p 6p change ☐ p

20p - 10p = ☐ p   20p - 5p = ☐ p

20p - 4p = ☐ p   20p - 2p = ☐ p

20p - 12p = ☐ p   20p - 13p = ☐ p

20p - 14p = ☐ p  20p - 15p = ☐ p

25

is longer than

is shorter than

Write longer or shorter.

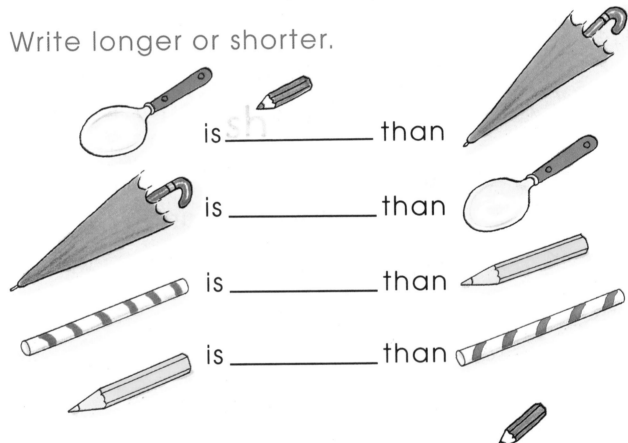

is _sh_____ than

is _____ than

is _____ than

is _____ than

Measure a straw with a ruler. _____ cm

Measure a spoon. _____ cm

Measure a crayon. _____ cm

Write **heavier** or **lighter**.

The elephant is _____ than the rabbit.

The rabbit is _____ than the elephant.

The mouse is _____ than the rabbit.

The rabbit is _____ than the mouse.

The elephant is _____ than the mouse.

The mouse is _____ than the elephant.

 Weigh some toys.

27

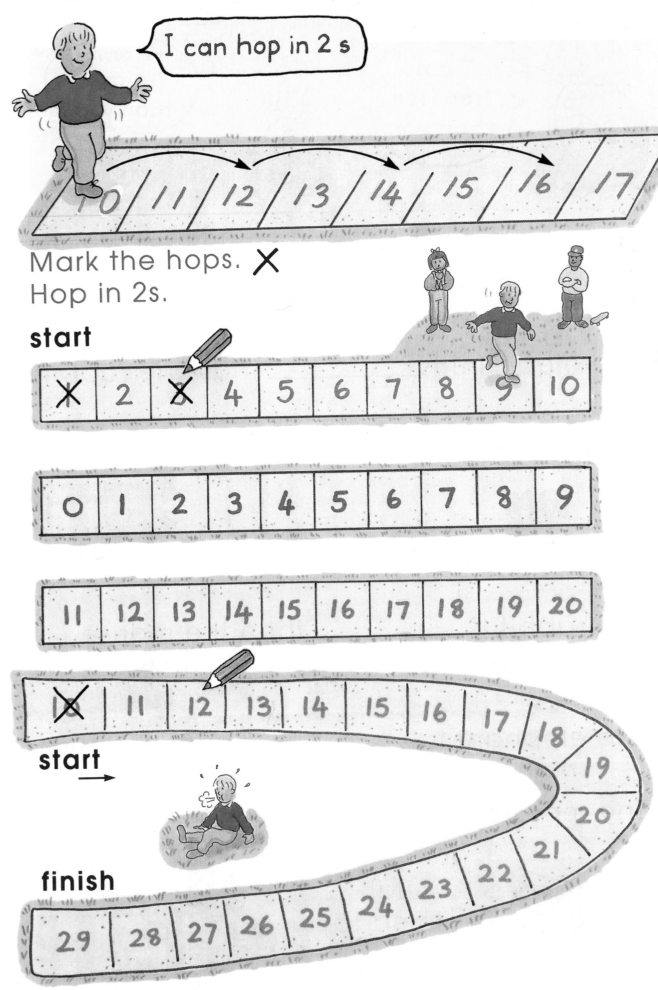

I can hop in 2 s

Mark the hops. ✗
Hop in 2s.

start

Pairs

one bear □  arms

□ legs

□ eyes

 two bears □ arms

□ legs

□ eyes

□ bears

one cart

t___
carts carts

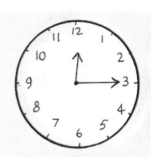 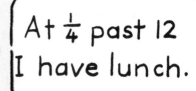 

At $\frac{1}{4}$ past 12 I have lunch.

 $\frac{1}{4}$ past     $\frac{1}{4}$ to [2]

 $\frac{1}{4}$ past [ ] $\frac{1}{4}$ to [ ]

 $\frac{1}{4}$ past [ ] $\frac{1}{2}$ past [ ]

 $\frac{1}{4}$ to [ ]    [ ] o'clock

Put the hands on.

My bedtime is 8 o'clock.

My breakfast time is $\frac{1}{2}$ past 7.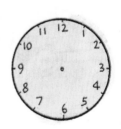

Months

December   August

month	number of days	
January	31	
February	28	sometimes 29
March	31	
April	30	
May	31	
June	30	
July	31	
August	31	
September	30	
October	31	
November	30	
December	31	

Bonfire night is the 5 th of _____ .

The months with 30 days are

___Ap_____   _____

_____   _____

My birthday is on the _____ of _____

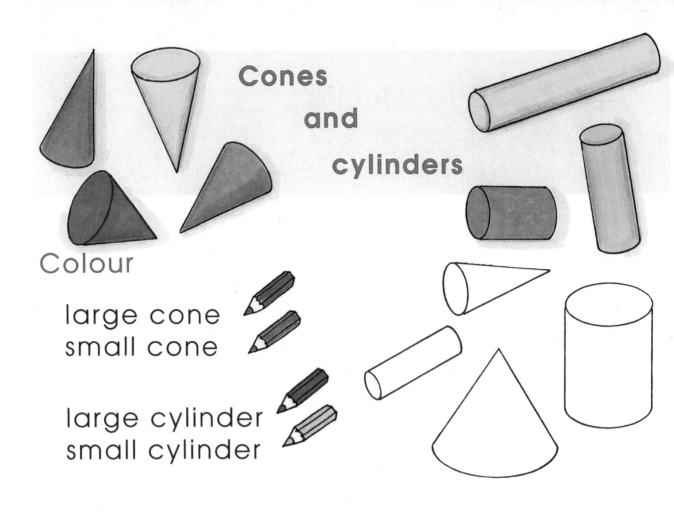

Cones and cylinders

Colour

    large cone

    small cone

    large cylinder

    small cylinder

Join the names to the shapes.

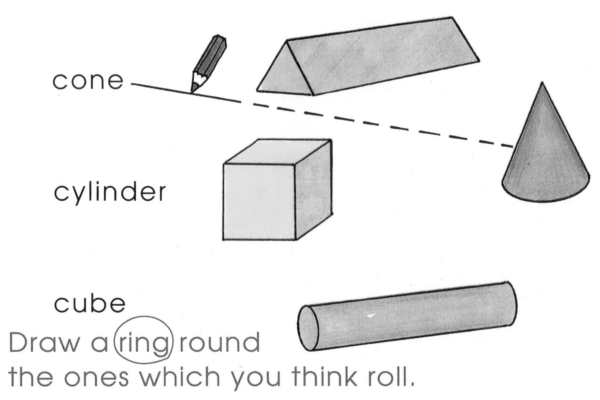

cone

cylinder

cube

Draw a (ring) round
the ones which you think roll.